LOOK
at the
Animals

by Brenda T. Owens

illustrated by Dave Klug

HOUGHTON MIFFLIN   BOSTON • MORRIS PLAINS, NJ

California • Colorado • Georgia • Illinois • New Jersey • Texas

Look at the elephant.
The elephant is here.

Look at the horses.
The horses are here.

Look at the ducks.
The ducks are here.

Look at the pigs.
The pigs are here.

Look at the birds.
The birds are here.

Look at the skunk.
The skunk is here.

Good - bye!